I'd do it all over, *again* and I'd do it *better*

A Caregiver's Journey Through Alzheimer's

A Memoir of My Husband, Carl J. Pfeifer,
and Stories of Our Journey Together
as a Caregiver and a Person with Alzheimer's

Janaan Manternach

Acknowledgments

I'd do it all over again and I'd do it better
A Caregiver's Journey Through Alzheimer's
Janaan Manternach

Copyright © 2020 Janaan Manternach

Published by ACTA Publications,
4848 N. Clark Street, Chicago, IL 60640

www.actapublications.com, 800-397-2282, all rights reserved.

**Cover Art
& Train Station
Inside Back Cover Art**
John August Swanson

Helped Update Article
Washington Post
August 4, 2007

Obituary
Telegraph Herald
Dubuque Iowa
July 15, 2007

Project Consultant
Dan Pierson

Copy Editor
Mary Carol Kendzia

Design and Development
RCL Benziger, a Kendall Hunt Company
Cincinnati Ohio

ISBN: 978-0-87946-969-6
Library of Congress Catalog Number: 2020943555
Printed in the United States of America by Total Printing Systems
Year 30 29 28 27 26 25 24 23 22 21 20
Printing 10 9 8 7 6 5 4 3 2 First

Printed on 30% post-consumer recycled paper

Dedication

I dedicate this book

to my beloved husband,

Carl J. Pfeifer,

who loved me as I was,

which enabled me to

become more and more

of whom I am.

Contents

I've been asked to write a preface so that readers who did not know us would get a glimpse of who we were and what we did during our professional lives. I decided to include the following column that was written by Matt Schudel and appeared in *The Washington Post* on August 4, 2007, shortly after Carl's death.

Carl J. Pfeifer, 78; Helped Update
By MATT SCHUDEL
Washington Post Staff Writer

Carl J. Pfeifer, 78, who resigned from the Catholic priesthood to marry his co-author, with whom he wrote a series of influential textbooks on Catholic education, died of Alzheimer's disease July 12 at Stonehill Care Center in Dubuque, Iowa. He lived in Arlington County until last year.

In 1968, Dr. Pfeifer was a Jesuit priest working at Catholic University when he and a Franciscan nun published the first of a series of textbooks for elementary students on Catholic education and catechism. The series, called "Life, Love, Joy," represented a dramatic change in the way Catholic school children learned about their faith.

Over the next 30 years, Dr. Pfeifer and Dr. Janaan Manternach revised their textbooks, wrote widely and traveled across the world to lead seminars on Catholic education. Their books and other classroom materials, published most recently under the title "This Is Our Faith," were used in Catholic schools in all 50 states. They replaced the old Baltimore catechism, a system of learning by rote, with a dynamic storytelling approach drawing on examples from everyday life.

"What Carl and I did, which was seen as a real change, was we introduced life experience to catechetical education," Manternach said yesterday. "If we're going to find God, we're going to find God in life."

After collaborating for 10 years, Dr. Manternach and Dr. Pfeifer felt a growing attraction that went beyond their shared work and faith. In their 40s, they went through the formal process of resigning from their religious orders. He had been a member of the Jesuits for 29 years; she had been a nun for 27.

Only then did they go on their first date. They had never so much as held hands before.

"We were absolutely in love with each other, there's no question, before that first date," Manternach said.

They were married Nov. 20, 1976, at Holy Trinity Catholic Church in Georgetown. Four priests officiated at the ceremony, and the 300 guests gave them a standing ovation, but their decision to marry was not warmly received by all.

One priest wrote a letter branding their actions "evil." Manternach's sister refused to attend the wedding, and a nun who had been a close friend said Manternach was now "dead" to her.

"Before that, I had a community," Manternach said yesterday. "Now, I had a community of one."

With little money and uncertain job prospects, the newly married couple settled in Arlington and returned to their mission of Catholic education. When the archbishop of Baltimore invited Dr. Pfeifer to speak at a conference on Catholic liturgy, they knew they had found official acceptance.

Dr. Pfeifer and Dr. Manternach revised their "Life, Love, Joy" series, wrote for magazines and published books for teachers. They taught courses on Catholic education and doctrine to seminarians and, from 1967 to 1992, appeared as panelists on the weekly "Bauman Bible Telecasts," a nationally televised college religion course based in Washington.

Catechism Education

They answered questions from religion teachers in a monthly newsletter from 1987 to 1998 and collected their columns in a book, "How to Be a Better Catechist." In 1987, they published "People to Remember," a book about inspirational Catholic figures, and they often spoke to groups of teachers, priests and parents.

From 1970 to 1979, Dr. Pfeifer wrote a weekly syndicated column, "Know Your Faith," for the National Catholic News Service. For several years, he wrote a second column, "Photomeditations," linking religious themes with photographs he had taken. He also wrote the "Core Beliefs" and "Did You Know?" columns for FaithWorks magazine from 1998 to 2002.

He "enjoyed audiences," Manternach said. "He liked to address the spirits of people, and their spirits often responded."

Carl Jacob Pfeifer was born June 22, 1929 in St. Louis and lived above his family's bakery, which was across the street from a Catholic church.

He graduated from St. Louis University and received a master's degree in philosophy from the university in 1954. He taught Latin and Greek at his alma mater's Jesuit high school for several years and continued his studies at Georgetown University, Laval University in Quebec City, Austria's Innsbruck University and St. Mary's College in Kansas before becoming an ordained priest in 1961. He received a doctorate in ministry from St. Mary's Seminary and University in Baltimore in 1985.

While teaching a course on the Psalms at Catholic University in the early 1960s, Dr. Pfeifer met Dr. Manternach, who had taught in Iowa and Chicago for 11 years. One day after class, she remarked that his classroom style was all wrong.

"Over the weekend, he changed his way of teaching the Psalms," she recalled. "He brought into play poetry; he added music; he brought in photographs he had taken. He used humanizing elements in his class."

Invited to work on a new model of religious training, they became assistant directors of the National Center for the Confraternity of Christian Doctrine at Catholic University and began their lifelong collaboration.

"It was an unexpected path," said Dr. Manternach, of Arlington, who survives her husband, along with one of his brothers. "Carl expected to be a professor at St. Louis University and go up the ladder from there. His career path was geared toward being a theology and Scripture professor."

To commemorate the textbook series that brought them together and formed their life's work, Dr. Pfeifer and Dr. Manternach had their wedding rings engraved with three words: "Life, Love, Joy."

Washington Post
Used with permission.
August 4, 2007

Preface

Reasons For Writing This Book

I had two reasons for writing the book, *I'd Do It All Over Again and I'd Do It Better*.

The first reason that I wanted to write the book is for my husband, Carl J. Pfeifer, to be remembered. He should be remembered not just for what he accomplished during his productive years as an author, professor, and photographer, but also for how he was during the nine years that he suffered from Alzheimer's.

The second reason is that as I grew into the challenges of being a caregiver, I wanted to use what I learned to help other caregivers. The greatest thing I learned is that I could do it, no matter what, and that I was not alone. A Divine Presence figured into that equation and I allude to it during those times when I became keenly aware that it made a difference. Caregiving is a process that unfolds in unique ways between what is going on in the lives of the person with Alzheimer's and his/her caregiver. My hope is that my story makes a significant and holy difference in the stories of other caregivers.

There are several things that are unique about my book, *I'd Do It All Over Again and I'd Do It Better*.

It's my story and because each of us is unique, my story is simply that: Unique. There will be some similarities in how Carl was as a person with Alzheimer's and how I was as a caregiver, but there will be big differences. Hopefully this book will help the reader recognize those differences in his or her situation, accept them, and grow in the process.

The chapters are reasonably short, creatively literate, and easy to read. Many of the people who received a first draft said they couldn't put the book down and read it in one sitting.

Janaan Manternach

Introduction

After Carl's death it took me awhile to accept that he was gone. So many memories haunted me, many of them good; many of them not so good. I kept wishing that I could do it all over again. Then the thought of telling our story, both to help me accept those feelings and help others do better as caregivers, occurred to me.

My story will, in many ways, be different from yours because each person with Alzheimer's is unique. Yet my story of caregiving may offer insights that might make a difference in how you act and respond as a caregiver.

The first and most important insight that I hope is evident throughout my story is that there is a Divine plan continually happening in both you and your loved one, be it a spouse, a parent, or someone other. In that belief there is an abiding trust that God is with us in all that is unfolding in our lives and that, no matter what, all will be well. The more you learn to trust the Divine plan the easier the journey may become.

The following are other insights that either I learned along the way or realized after Carl's death.

⌘ When Alzheimer's was initially happening in Carl there was a tendency in me to resist the changes. I didn't want to adjust. I didn't want to do for him what he no longer could do for himself. If that happens in you, know that you can adjust; know that you have inner powers that you were not aware that you have. Your better angels take over and you grow, particularly in kindness, which is probably one of the best things that can happen.

ᗧ There were times when I failed miserably and that may happen to you, too. I hope that you learn from my story to let go of those times. Refuse to dwell on the misery that both of you may be experiencing, learn from it and move on.

ᗧ Creativity will often come into play when an unexpected change occurs in your loved one's behavior. Surprisingly, you'll find yourself knowing how to handle the situation differently – one that graciously meets both of your needs. This is a perfect example of Divine intervention, a time when you've grown in goodness.

ᗧ There is a lot of mystery in this insight but in spite of the significant losses that are now a part of your loved one's life there is still a lot going on. This may become evident when he or she cooperates in a situation where he or she was unable to before; or gives evidence of enjoying something in the moment; or "out of the blue" utters a phrase that reveals an awareness of what is going on.

ᗧ Perhaps more than any other discovery that can happen in a relationship between a person with Alzheimer's and a caregiver is how powerful love is. Taking time to reflect on what happened during each day will often reveal how many of your responses were caring, unselfish, thoughtful, and genuinely loving. Concentrating on those will give you the wherewithal and wisdom to become more and more loving, and will help you be grateful for the opportunity to be loving and to be a caregiver.

ᗧ Too late I discovered how important it is to accept offers of help. I strongly recommend that you let others participate in your caregiving story. Say "Yes" often. It will not only be a gift to you, it will also be a gift to them.

Chapter 1
First Signs of Alzheimer's

I've often been asked the question, What are the first noticeable signs of Alzheimer's? particularly by friends who are concerned that someone in their family is beginning to suffer from the disease, or by someone who is concerned about his or her own lapses in memory. Some of the concerns expressed were constantly misplacing keys, glasses, hearing aids, or other items. Another concern was related to someone going somewhere and becoming confused about where the person was going, and then having difficulty finding his or her way back. Still other concerns were frequently unable to find the words a person wanted to say during a conversation, forgetting appointments, experiencing mood changes, or having a son or daughter who worried about their lapses in memory.

The question is not an easy one to answer because I believe that Alzheimer's symptoms may differ from patient to patient. Some of the signs that concern someone may simply be related to aging.

Carl's and my situation was somewhat unique in that our work kept us talking to each other a lot during each work day, whether about a manuscript, a presentation, or a workshop. Most of our other talking was at dinnertime. For example, during breakfast we'd often be reading newspapers. At lunch, if we were hungry, we'd make a sandwich, a bowl of soup, or choose a piece of fruit and continue to read the newspapers. During dinner, we talked about the other parts of our lives that were not work related. At times we also watched the Lehrer Report on PBS, but mostly we really enjoyed the "getting in touch" that dinnertimes provided.

Admittedly, there were significant signs along the way that we both ignored because our work lives went on pretty much as usual. Carl continued to write, and we continued doing workshops and giving talks – mostly together, so that if there were slips on Carl's part I probably filled in. Neither the audience, nor we, seemed to pick up on those slips. There was also significant time between the development of various signs, which is also another reason we didn't know dementia or Alzheimer's was occurring in Carl. This, I believe, is not unusual.

Below are three of the significant signs that both of us missed and one that caught our attention.

Sign One

One of these signs was evident during a day of talks that Carl and I gave to priests in the Diocese of Tampa, Florida. It was in the late 1990s, after the *Catechism of the Catholic Church* was published. Carl gave the first talk in the morning on the *Catechism* and I gave the second.

In the afternoon, I presented first, and he conducted the final session. He completed his two sessions seemingly well, but much later when I was remembering the day, I realized that he wasn't always "tracking." There were gaps in what he was presenting – not major ones – but noticeable enough that I felt the priests were also aware of them. At the moment I had been too concerned with my part in the day to take serious notice. We returned home and went back to our usual lives.

Sign Two: A Year or More Later

Carl was scheduled to give a presentation on the sacraments to a group of catechumens at Holy Trinity Church, our parish, in Georgetown, Washington D.C. We were part of the RCIA (Rite of Christian Initiation of Adults) team preparing candidates who wished to become Catholic. Carl spent hours preparing for the session, so much so, that I went into his office twice to ask him why he was spending so much time on it. I felt he could do the session without any preparation, but he kept working on it.

The evening he was to give the talk, we gathered in the room with the candidates and the rest of the team. The room quieted as Carl was about to begin. He opened his mouth but nothing came out. His papers fell to the floor and for a moment no one quite knew what was happening. Then a nun on the team got Carl a glass of water; two others on the team took over the session, and the evening continued. What is amazing to me now is that, although Carl and I talked about what had happened, we didn't consider that something serious might be going on in Carl's brain. Again, we went on with our lives, as usual.

Sign Three: Much Later

Carl normally didn't speak up in social and business meetings, but if he had something to say he said it, and if he were questioned or asked to comment further, he would elaborate. This changed and became apparent during a meeting in which I knew he had plenty to say. When he didn't speak up, I asked him what he thought. He gave me a puzzled look and then said something meaningful about the issue, but it was apparent that he wasn't comfortable. I questioned him about it later and he didn't seem to remember the incident at all. I didn't sleep well that evening because I couldn't figure out what had happened yet. The next day, we again went on as usual.

Sign Four: This Time We Did Take Notice

It happened during a meeting of a discussion group where we were to share our feelings about an assigned book. This one challenged a lot of beliefs that, as Catholics, we had formerly held sacred. Prior to the meeting of the discussion group, both Carl and I, as we read the book, were surprised by how much in tune we were with the author. We talked about the fact that others in the group would not be on the same page, and in fact, probably in total disagreement with the author. We further discussed, in depth, what we would say that confirmed our beliefs.

At the meeting, I spoke first and waited for Carl to continue in the same vein. He didn't. He was totally on a different page from what we had discussed. It both shocked and upset me. This simply was not Carl. He always had my back, and when we planned something together, like we had for that meeting, we could count on each other to totally follow through. This time, he repeated what another in the group had said, which did not at all support what I had said.

Fortunately, I began to realize that Carl had no memory of what we had discussed and that I could not hold him accountable. With a sadness that was memorably deep, I realized something was happening in Carl's mind that made it less dependable for both him and me. On the way home, we didn't talk about what had happened, but the next day we broached the subject. Carl remembered nothing of the meeting, but he admitted that something was happening in his memory.

We finally acknowledged the symptoms and made an appointment with a neurologist. This was not as easy a step as I expected. The first neurologist that we contacted was helpful but genuinely unsure that Carl had Alzheimer's. He did, however, prescribe medication that I truly believe slowed the progress of the disease. A friendship developed with this neurologist that made it possible for me to call him anytime I had a question or a change occurred in Carl's behavior. He also recommended other doctors who were dealing specifically with dementia.

For nearly all the years Carl suffered from seeming mindlessness, none of the physicians gave us a definitive diagnosis of Alzheimer's until a doctor in Dubuque, Iowa simply said, "He has Alzheimer's." I was relieved, but by then, it didn't really make a difference in how Carl and I had come to live or in how we had been prior to his diagnosis.

The way each of us acknowledges the presence of Alzheimer's in our spouse or another family member will be different. Signs will often be present, but the circumstances of our lives will predict how we respond to them, as was the case in our situation. I now believe that the way we respond is predicated by our pattern of response in other major challenges in our lives. Ultimately, it is possible to see it as simply part of a Divine plan, and therefore, good.

Chapter 2
Accepting Inner Change

Your own inner change is probably the most powerful and unexpected result of being a caregiver to an Alzheimer's patient. These are a few of the steps that came about with my own inner change in caring for Carl.

1. Change Happens Gradually

Inner change truly happened gradually in me. I was initially resistant, not only to what was happening in Carl but also to the possibility of entering into a new relationship with him that would require much more than I wanted to give. I was genuinely happy with his ability, up to this point, to take care of himself and to be an equal partner in our life's work, which was authoring books and articles, presenting at conferences and workshops, and teaching as catechists and professors.

2. You May be Resistant to Change

How resistant I was to a change in our relationship became apparent early on in our new life together as caregiver and a person with Alzheimer's. One morning Carl dressed himself completely, as he had always done, but was unable to put on his shoes. This totally baffled and upset me, so much so that when he showed me that he couldn't put on his shoes, I let him know, in no uncertain terms, that I wasn't going to help him. He was a little nonplussed with my reaction, but he took his shoes and put them on – but on the wrong feet. That upset me more. I roughly took his shoes off and put them on the right feet.

Carl was hurt by the whole exchange, and a feeling of genuine remorse surged in me. I suddenly realized that a deep well of selfishness existed in me and that that quality might become a real problem in how we were going to handle together what was going on in him. Yet becoming aware of my selfish behavior created an immediate change. I felt shame, which in that instance was a healthy precursor. I determined that if he continued to need help putting his shoes on, which he did, I would do it for him kindly and graciously. I learned from that experience that I had the power to be unselfish.

3. Acceptance of Change Is Critical

Acceptance can be powerful and almost always happens unexpectedly. One example in Carl's and my journey happened early on. After evening meals, while I would be putting dishes in the dishwasher, Carl would always take the garbage out to a can in the back of the house. On this particular evening he was gone longer than usual, and I went outside to check. I found him standing on the patio with the garbage bag at his feet, looking utterly lost.

Amazingly, I was at my best self and I said to him, lovingly, "It's okay, it's okay!" and I took the garbage and deposited it in the can. I returned to where he was still standing, took him by the hand, and we re-entered the house. When we got into the house, Carl looked at me and said, "I'm losing my mind." With that we held each other and cried. Both of us knew that the time of denial was over. We were in a completely new place with the disease. This was an instance of inner change occurring in both of us at the same time.

4. Acceptance Isn't Easy

Another instance of a needed change in me happened with our daily walks. Both of us had a habit of taking a daily walk, but not together. My walks were more for exercise, and I liked to walk fast, mostly to do it and get it over with. Carl, on the other hand, enjoyed leisurely walks during which he talked to the squirrels and birds (literally), often with his camera around his neck. It was a time during the day when he could get away from his desk and simply enjoy nature and its beauty.

Gradually, I noticed that he had stopped taking his walks. At the same time, I started to feel that he shouldn't go off on his own. I offered to walk with him, but I told him upfront that I liked to walk fast. We decided to try to walk together. We walked out our front door, down the steps and I took off. He followed, but he couldn't keep up. Carl asked me to slow down, which I did, but not for long. In trying to keep up, he tripped and fell. I heard him fall and I looked back to see him down on the sidewalk. His hands and knees were bleeding, and he was hurting.

I helped him up and took him to a friend's home nearby. She helped me clean up Carl and we put bandages on his cuts, which fortunately weren't deep. I told him I was sorry for going so fast. He was utterly kind about what had happened, but I felt a kind of remorse that I had never before known. From then on, we continued daily walks but always hand-in-hand and at his pace.

What I realized from that experience is that my selfishness was such that I really didn't want to give up walking by myself – I really didn't want to take him for walks. I needed to change that attitude and I did. When that kind of awareness, that kind of change, takes place in our behavior we grow and become a far better person.

5. Acceptance Can Be Creative

Later, when Carl could no longer take a shower and dress himself, I'd get up, take a shower, and dress myself. Then I'd wake him, help him bathe, and get dressed. By the time I was finished getting him ready, however, I was perspiring and in need of another shower.

One morning it dawned on me that I should get him up first, help him shower and dress, place him in a comfortable chair, and then take care of myself. That worked perfectly. I was surprised by– and grateful for – how well I handled that situation. What continually amazed and surprised me during my days of caring for Carl was how capable I was of changing, in spite of how much I liked being independent, and how hardheaded I naturally am.

6. Acceptance Can Ease and Overcome Loneliness

For the most part, I was fine during the day while caring for Carl because his presence was real, and I was not alone. When he was in bed and asleep before me, however, my mind became more aware of his "goneness," and I found myself unable to do anything productive. A number of times I had bouts of sheer panic. At these times I'd simply join him in bed because somehow, I had to be with him.

Yet I knew this was not a solution to my loneliness. One night, I talked myself into accepting what I couldn't change and worked productively on a project. From that night on, I realized that there was enough strength in me to do what I needed and wanted to do. It was the kind of acceptance that was freeing and fulfilling.

7. Acceptance, at Times, Demands Radical Change

How I handled another instance still surprises me. For a long time I went to lunch weekly with one of my friends. Before I left, I would fix lunch for Carl, sit with him while he ate, and then place him comfortably in his recliner. I'd tell him that I was going to lunch with Susan or Maureen, and that I'd be back in an hour and a half. He seemed to understand, even seemed happy for me.

When I would return from these lunches he was often asleep or simply relaxing in his recliner. But one afternoon when I returned, he was at the door when I opened it, and very agitated. No matter how much I told him about where I had been I could not ease his anxiety. That was the last time I left him alone. From then on, I took him with me or had someone stay with him while I did what I wanted or needed to do. Mysteriously, I accepted this loss of independence totally and lovingly. At the time I didn't realize how much of a change, how much growth had occurred in me, but now I do and I am grateful.

8. Acceptance Can Be a Two-Way Street

One day, when we had an appointment with one of his physicians, I got Carl ready and we walked to the car. I opened the door on the passenger side so that he could get in. He stood absolutely still. I urged him to get into the car. I begged him, but he wouldn't or couldn't. He wasn't at all overweight, but he was tall and lanky. In no way was I strong enough to lift him into the seat. Finally, I gave up and we walked back into the house. I helped him into his recliner, called the doctor's office, and canceled the appointment. Then I sat at the dining room table and cried. I felt both helpless and utterly hopeless.

The next time I needed him to get into the car, however, I prepared him ahead of time by telling him where we were going, when we had to be there, and that he would have to get into the car. I gently asked him if he thought that he could get into the car and he nodded, "Yes." When we got to the car he hesitated for a few seconds, then got in. I was so relieved that I reached over and hugged him. He somehow sensed that I desperately needed him to do it, and he did it. This was an instance when I realized that there was still much going on in Carl and that it needed to be recognized and celebrated, if only with a hug.

9. Inner Change Enhances

Perhaps one of the greatest outcomes in the Alzheimer's journey is a growth in goodness. The Divine in each of us is enlivened with each change that occurs both in us and in the one who is in our care. That enhancement of the Divine increases our ability to accept our situation and act in a loving manner.

Chapter 3
Developing a Positive Attitude

Part of what happened in me as I recovered from the shock, the disbelief, and the feelings of hopelessness that surfaced when I realized that Carl had Alzheimer's was a comforting awareness that he was more than his mind. This was huge because Carl's mind had always been front and center in both our personal and professional lives. As I was processing the realization that he was more than his mind, I wasn't sure what kind of difference it was going to make in our everyday lives because there was still a lot going on in his mind. He was still writing; we were still communicating easily, and life was pretty much normal.

Letting Go

What did follow, which was good, was getting rid of feelings of anger and shame, but most of all getting rid of questions like, "Why did this happen to us?" and "How will we cope?" Instead, a healthy attitude emerged out of nowhere. We told our family and friends what was going on. Some were taken aback, some had suspected, some were sure it wasn't happening, and some knew. For example, our goddaughter, Angela, had gone for a walk with Carl and later wrote about it:

> My godfather, who was like a second dad, started forgetting things. We took a walk one day. I led easy conversations so he wouldn't have to rely on his memory. After a bit of talking, we walked in silence.
>
> Then, Carl turned to me and said, "Angela, something's happening to me, isn't it? I know it is." I did everything possible not to start bawling in front of him. Instead, I took his hand and said. "Yes,

Carl. it is. You are in the early stages of Alzheimer's. That means that your brain is going to start deteriorating and it will get harder and harder for you to remember things."

"Why?" he asked.

I wanted to shout, "I don't know! It's so unfair!!!" Instead, I said, "I don't know, Carl. I wish it weren't happening, but some things happen we can't control. I wish you didn't have Alzheimer's. But no matter what, I will always love you."

I hugged him. He hugged back tightly and gave a deep sigh. We both were a little teary-eyed when we pulled away. We walked, holding hands, the rest of the way.

When Angela told me about this exchange with Carl, I felt real sadness but also a deeper acknowledgment of what was happening in him. It made me newly aware of the losses he was experiencing and that I had to let go of wanting him to be more than he could be. It was clearly another instance of Divine intervention that was saving and, actually, energizing.

Continuing to Do "the Usual"

For some mysterious reason, in spite of the losses, I knew that we would continue to accept invitations to social events. This was not necessarily easy for Carl because he had never been all that great at socializing before Alzheimer's, so now it was even harder. Yet, we did it.

When we were out, I always stayed close by him, and never left him alone. The best part of it was that our friends were grateful that we continued to be part of the occasions. It kept us in the loop, which was vital for me and, surprisingly, also for Carl. Those events seemed to enliven him. He rarely remembered our friend's names, but he remembered *them*. Instances like that made me acutely and delightfully aware that there was still much going on in his mind that needed to be continually trusted and tended.

Probably the greatest gift we were given is that our care for each other stayed stable and strong. This may be a truism in a caregiving relationship, but something continued to go on between us which can only be stated in the phrase, "He was mine and I was his." This truly was the basis for being able to meet each challenge, each change, as it happened.

One challenge that we encountered seems minor now, but at the time it had seemed major. I had always thought that game shows on television were a sheer waste of time. For some mysterious reason, however, Carl developed a liking for them. He wanted to watch them but not alone. When they were on, he was always looking to see where I was. I finally decided to make them a priority. We watched them together evening after evening. Gradually I found that I liked them, too. It became a special time of being with each other.

Developing a positive attitude toward the reality of Alzheimer's in our lives happened only because of a truth that is part of my religious belief. That is, I believe there is a Divine plan continually going on in each of our lives, and that God is with us through it all.

Chapter 4
Helping to Lower Expectations

One of the hardest adjustments in a relationship between an Alzheimer's patient and a caregiver is to lower expectations of what we can and cannot accomplish. What used to be is, in many ways, no longer. I found myself living with someone new, yet I also kept getting glimpses of Carl as he had always been. We kept talking to each other – actually, that never stopped. Now. however, it was different. There was less depth, and our conversations were less frequent, but for some incredible, wondrous reason, we kept communicating.

Diminishments continued to occur and, admittedly, I found each one a surprise. I know that at times, Carl was also taken aback by these changes, and both of us had to find a way to cope. Coping, for me, required attitude changes, and most of them meant ridding myself of another bit of selfishness. I had to keep finding answers to the question, "Can I do this?"

It's still hard for me to understand the internal loss that a person feels when he or she can't fully dress themselves. Except for being unable to put on his shoes, which I described in Chapter Two, Carl was able to totally dress himself. But one morning he couldn't. I had to step up and dress him, and he had to adjust to this limitation of not being able to dress himself.

Sadly, there was still enough going on in his mind that needing someone to dress him made Carl feel diminished. He cooperated completely, but there was an expression of loss on his face that still haunts me at times. Fortunately, this made me act kindly as I was dressing him. It simply became a daily ritual. Working out the right time, as I mention in Chapter Two – helping him take a shower and dressing him *before* I showered and dressed – was all part of dealing unselfishly and kindly with changes in his grooming.

Other Issues

Early on, it became apparent that Carl wasn't always aware of when he had to go to the bathroom. This was partly taken care of by the use of disposable undergarments. I also put him on a schedule for taking him to the bathroom, which worked well most of the time. In one instance, however, I put him on the stool and sat on the side of the tub while I waited for him to urinate. He sat there but didn't do anything. Then he simply stood up and peed on the floor. I didn't handle this very well. Later, with great remorse, I realized that when he had to pee he didn't sit on the stool; he stood near it. It is one of those times when, if I had a chance to do it over, I would do it better.

For a long time, I could go to my office on the second floor of our home while Carl dozed in his recliner on the first floor. But one scary day, I came down from my office and he wasn't in his recliner – nor was he anywhere else in the house. Fortunately, a neighbor, who knew of our situation, ran into him as he was walking aimlessly in the neighborhood and met me, with Carl in tow, as I came out of our door to search for him.

From then on, when he rested in his recliner in the living room I worked at my computer nearby in the dining room. It was an adjustment because I didn't have everything I needed readily at hand, but I was able to accomplish pretty much everything that I needed to do. This required running back and forth to my upstairs office, but I decided that was good exercise and I became totally okay with it – even happy.

Carl was on Advair, an inhaler to help him breathe, for many years. Every day he automatically took it into his hands, put it up to his lips, and breathed in and out the prescribed number of times. Eventually, he could no longer do this on his own. I began to hold the inhaler up to his lips, and at first he responded very well. But one day Carl didn't understand that he had to breathe in and out. I called his physician, and he told me to stop using the inhaler. That worried me, but amazingly, perhaps because of that mysterious reality, Divine intervention, Carl continued to breathe well without it.

Another change was with reading newspapers. Carl had always thoroughly enjoyed reading various newspapers, including the *National Catholic Reporter* and the magazine, *America*. He'd often read through them when he finished work, usually around five o'clock, or after dinner. I'd often read them when they arrived in the morning or at lunch time.

One day, I noticed him pick up a newspaper, put it aside, and walk away from the coffee table where the newspapers were lying. For some graceful reason, I didn't say anything – I didn't ask if there was something wrong. Yet innately I knew that another diminishment had occurred. Later that week, when *America* arrived in the mail, I handed it to him. He glanced at the cover and then quietly set it aside. I adjusted to that change by cancelling all of the newspapers but one. I would tell him about the current events. He was still interested in hearing the news, but simply unable to continue reading it.

No Longer Driving

The greatest and most devastating change for me happened when he was no longer able to drive. Carl loved to drive, and he had an uncanny ability to drive anywhere we needed to go – he didn't need GPS! This all changed one day when we were driving on a local street. All of a sudden, he turned the car into the oncoming lane. Fortunately, there wasn't much traffic. He really resisted, but I was able to get him back into the right lane.

In that instance, I knew that had to be the end of Carl driving – and it was. Yet that loss wasn't only painful to me. Carl still wanted to drive and couldn't understand why I wouldn't let him. The biggest change and loss for both of us were the limitations his inability to drive now placed on our travel plans. We were no longer able to take long trips to visit relatives or drive to other places that weren't local. I was able to drive in our immediate area but not much beyond.

At least once or twice a week we went out for lunch because it got both of us out of the house. We usually went to Carl's favorite restaurant – the Metro Diner. He always ordered the same entrée, a ham and cheese omelet. That changed one day when he looked at the menu and was totally confused. In frustration, he handed it to me. I ordered for him, but I was so taken aback that I totally lost my appetite. Sometimes I was able to quickly adapt to changes, but sometimes I was not. Eventually I did adapt to this change and we continued to go to lunch, but Carl never used the menu again.

Dealing with change is doable. The lowering of expectations not only affects the caregiver, it also affects the person with Alzheimer's. This process is neither predictable nor is it the same in everyone who has the disease. Everyone is *unique*. No one of us is like another.

I shared with you some of what happened in Carl's and my story. There will be differences in your story, but what will not be different is that changes continually occur and adjustments have to be made. Mysteriously, it all becomes doable; oftentimes it makes us more gracious, kinder, and above all, more loving. It can be a gift.

Chapter 5
Focus on the Person

How do you keep your focus on the person, and not on the disease when you are caring for someone with Alzheimer's? Dealing with the answer to this question demands a recognition that the person and the disease are one. It affects not just the "who" of the person but the "how" he or she has always been.

Carl did not find the losses he was experiencing in his mind and memory easy. He sensed he was "losing his mind" (his own words). This both frightened and worried him, to the extent that he could fathom what was happening. It also frightened and worried me because, in many ways, especially in the functioning of our professional lives, he was truly "Commander in Chief."

Carl was something of a genius in meeting deadlines, partly because he relished work-related challenges. Since meeting deadlines was a major part of our work lives, his ability along those lines was sheer gift. Truthfully, I carried my part of our workload, but knowing that I was working with someone who was truly on top of things no matter what they entailed added much to my joy and peace. In all of it we were truly a team that was unbelievably productive. What I expected to go on and on, more or less, came to a rather sudden slowdown and ultimately, a complete halt.

I sadly remember one day when I took Carl back to his computer, hoping that he would find respite there. He sat down at his desk where he had worked happily and productively for years. As though by habit, Carl put his fingers on the keys of his computer. Nothing happened! He then held his fingers momentarily in midair, and suddenly, in bewilderment, put his hands down and pushed himself away from his desk. He looked at me with an unforgettable emptiness in his eyes that wordlessly asked the question, "What is going on?"

With tears in my eyes I helped him up from his chair, took him back downstairs, and sat him in his recliner. He immediately fell asleep, which I believe was one of the wonders of the disease.

Alzheimer's truly robbed Carl of the loss of being able to do something. But it also graciously and immediately robbed him of the pain of remembering the loss.

It also gave me time to adjust to what had just occurred. I cried hard, but only for a few moments. I then did what I do a lot. I talked to myself about what had just happened, and found myself saying, "Obviously Carl's mind is not working like it used to." I actually kept repeating that to myself. It was not a new revelation, but my mind was having a hard time accepting the obvious.

The next step happened at a more subconscious level than conscious level, but I had some realization that the Carl I was now living with was a new Carl with a disease that was robbing him of thinking and acting like he did when his mind was healthy and well. He was still my husband, my best friend, a vital presence -- someone whose heart, spirit, and body were still operative. The disease does gradually affect the whole person, but only *gradually*.

Living Out the Truth Day-to-Day

I actually found myself saying anew to myself what I had often said before, "I am not just my mind. I am more than that and so is Carl." I also realized, painfully, that that was easier to say than to live it out in the day-to-day. But with frequent missteps along the way I did live out that truth about Carl each day.

One of the things that I did was simple. Every day I dressed Carl in fresh clothes – underwear, socks, shirt, pants, sweater or jacket. He always looked handsome. His appearance added to the greatness of his presence.

Another opportunity to enhance Carl's presence involved the NPCD Emmaus Award (National Association of Parish Catechetical Directors) that we were awarded for excellence in catechesis. The award ceremony would be held on April 19, 2001 in Milwaukee, Wisconsin. As part of the presentation, we were each expected to give a talk on some area of catechesis.

When we received word that we had been selected, I was both excited and grateful, but unsure about Carl's participation. Gradually, it dawned on me that I could write his talk, which I did. I read it with him over and over again until he was able to read it on his own. I sat on the stool by the grand piano in our living room as his audience; he stood on the opposite side of the piano, placed the talk on top of it, and read what I had written. We did that every day until he was totally comfortable.

When the time came for Carl to make his presentation at the awards ceremony, before a large audience that included members of my family from Iowa and members of his from Missouri, he did it perfectly, even using gestures as he talked. No one in the audience was aware that he had Alzheimer's, except for family and a few friends. It was a perfect example of the truth about Alzheimer's, that there is often more that remains of the person's capabilities than seems likely. It is vitally important to continually draw on that likelihood.

I am not sure how all of what I did happened because the selfishness in me is deep and sometimes troublesome, but nearly always I treated Carl with gentleness and respect. There were real lapses in my behavior at times, but I loved him deeply and he loved me too. It's in a challenge like Alzheimer's that we discover, learn, and experience how powerful love is.

During the nine years that Carl had Alzheimer's, I never, ever tired of his presence. There were many very real challenges and hardships caused by the disease, but we dealt with them and life went on. The one thing that never changed was his life-giving presence: *that* was a sheer gift to me. I know, too, that my presence was life-giving and a sheer gift to him.

Chapter 6

The Gift of Others in Our Lives

During most of the years that Carl had Alzheimer's, he and I were living in Arlington, Virginia. My mom and brothers and sister were living in Cascade and Dubuque, Iowa, while Carl's brother and family were living in St. Louis, Missouri. They were concerned for us but were unable to be with us in the everyday activities of our new lives. There were many other people – friends, co-workers in our parish community, and neighbors – who never gave up offering to help and to be with us in any way that we might need.

Our greatest support throughout the eight years of caregiving in our home were our godchildren, Angela and Miguel, and their parents, with whom we were very close. When Angela and Miguel's dad, Bill, had completed five years as Country Director of the Peace Corps in Belize, Central America, and had returned to Arlington he told us that he and his wife, Blanca, would come to our home every Thursday evening with appetizers and dinner. Many times, Angela and Miguel, two young people who Carl loved dearly, would join us. They would engage him in conversation and laughter.

Mysteriously, Carl was attentive to everything that we talked about and frequently added his two cents worth, which delighted all of us. Bill and Blanca knew and prepared the foods he particularly enjoyed, which added much to each of the evenings. This was a time each week to celebrate Carl for whom he was right then, and not for what he had been. He sensed the total acceptance of him by everyone present, and he loved it. It truly was the best of times.

How much Carl enjoyed it became apparent the night after the first evening that Bill and Blanca treated us. I had made dinner and we were seated at the table when Carl looked at me and asked, "Where is everybody?" I was amused and surprised, and told him gently that we weren't going to have company every evening; for that evening I was "everybody."

Angela often left fresh pastries at our door when she went to work, and I'd find them when I opened the door to pick up the paper. She also frequently reminded me that if I ever needed to talk she was always available.

Not just once in a while but almost every day, Bill would call and say, "I'm just ten minutes away. Could I stop by for a few minutes?" Those times were often life-saving for me. He would visit with Carl, which gave me time to do something that I wanted to do on my own or just do nothing. It also made me keenly aware that to continue visiting with someone who has Alzheimer's confers on them a respect that enlivens whatever still remains. Bill never presumed that Carl couldn't converse with him, so they were always chatting away.

Bill also stayed with Carl when I had an appointment or was meeting with a friend or needed to get groceries. He would often take him for a walk or a ride to some place he knew might be familiar to Carl. For instance, we had been consultants to the Leadership Committee of Religious Education at Good Shepherd Parish in Mount Vernon, Virginia for three years. One afternoon when Bill was with Carl, he took him to Mount Vernon, drove into the parish grounds, and talked to him about the work we had done there. When they returned Carl looked like a new person. Much of what he saw at Good Shepherd that day somehow stirred memories and gladdened his spirit.

Others Who Helped

Angela's and Miguel's mom, Leyda, and her husband, Dana, were also a critical part of our support system. Often on Sundays, as well as other evenings, they invited us to dinner. Their home was a place where Carl sensed that he was totally welcome, just the way he was. There were no expectations of him except that he enjoy the food and the company. He could tell that Leyda and Dana loved having us with them. I learned, particularly, from those evenings, that feelings are vitally alive in those who have Alzheimer's, and that treating those feelings with respect, affection, and care helps Alzheimer's patients feel good about themselves.

I believe that helping individuals with Alzheimer's to feel good about themselves is one of the most important things we and others can do in our roles as caregivers, family, and friends.

When a close friend, Maureen Riddel, who was also a nurse, learned that I needed to have surgery, she moved into our home. She not only took care of Carl, but she also took care of me. She was a total godsend.

People who were part of our parish offered again and again to help. Our next-door neighbor, Ursula Shean, offered to be with Carl when I needed to be away. Angela's and Miguel's aunt, Odeth, was also eager to be of help.

I didn't respond as well as I might have to the many offers. I regarded these offers as "insurance," offers that I would accept when I really needed them. Yet looking back, I should have accepted more of the offers than I did, and I strongly recommend that offers be seriously considered and frequently accepted. It's often as much a gift to the givers as it is to us, the persons with Alzheimer's and/or the caregivers.

Chapter 7
Experiencing Loss

The closer we are to someone who has Alzheimer's the more aware we become of the power and the ravages this disease has on the person suffering from it.

Amazingly, throughout the years that Carl suffered from Alzheimer's he never gave up trying to communicate, although in lucid moments, he knew that it was a major battle, one that he couldn't win. For example, one day he was trying to tell me something and I was eagerly listening because I wanted to hear what he was going to say. Nothing came out and suddenly, he looked at me and clearly spoke these awful words, "Please help me! I'm slipping away."

In that moment, Carl's face registered a hopelessness that I will never forget. It was a moment in which we both had an insight into how robbed he felt of the ability to keep in touch verbally, of being able to say what he wanted to share. He was no longer able to communicate what was on his mind; his brain was no longer able to process what he was thinking. Gone was an anchor, a mooring that kept him connected with me and with others.

It was a moment of critical discernment for me. He was still thinking; some parts of his brain were still active. He was simply unable to put all or any of what he was thinking into words. This is a painful loss, one that is a hallmark of the disease.

Another instance happened one morning when I went to my computer to work. Carl followed me and stood by helplessly. This annoyed me. I told him I had work to get done, and that he should go and sit in his recliner downstairs. He reluctantly, did but ten minutes later, he was again standing by me looking totally lost.

Fortunately, my reaction at that moment was a generous one. I pulled up a comfortable chair, placed it near my desk, and invited him to join me. A smile broke over his face as he sat down. I told him what I was doing. Amazingly, there was still something going on in his brain and he offered some suggestions. I was both surprised and grateful, and we both reveled in that. From then on, he sat by me while I worked. It didn't matter that he often fell asleep. What mattered for him was that he wasn't alone – and I wasn't alone either.

Another incident occurred that caught me totally off guard and happened unexpectedly. We had flown from Washington, DC to Dubuque to attend a family event. On the morning we were to return to Washington, we ate breakfast and waited for my sister, Grace, and her friend, John Donahue, to take us to the airport. Suddenly Carl realized that we were going somewhere. He looked at me with utter fear in his eyes and said, "I can't go! I can't go." I told him that we had to leave, that we had airline tickets and had to be home for another commitment. He insisted that he couldn't and became rigid in his chair.

I begged Carl; I pleaded with him. I was about to give up when Grace and John arrived and quickly noticed what was going on. Very gently John took Carl by both hands, helped him up from his chair, and guided him to the car. We then took off. When we got to the airport Carl was totally cooperative, seemingly not remembering what had happened earlier. I was worried what might happen when we had to change planes in Chicago, but again, he was fine. When we arrived in D.C., close friends met us and all was well.

Fear and panic are two ravages that can cause surprise and create distress for both the individual with Alzheimer's and the caregiver. During these circumstances, when they occurred in Carl, an outsider (my sister's friend), distracted him and erased what was causing his inability to deal with the moment. In this instance, as was true of others, when the moment passed Carl's brain became free of what was bedeviling it. Over time, knowing this helped me accept more gracefully the unexpected that is truly part of the disease.

Chapter 8

Regrets Are Part of Our Story

It was September 30, 2006. Carl was now living at Stonehill, a nursing home in Dubuque, Iowa. Our goddaughter, Angela, and her husband, Jeff, were in Dubuque visiting us. We had been with Carl during the afternoon and while he ate dinner. We took him back to his room, and I think he was expecting us to spend the evening with him, as I usually did. But I had made plans with Angela and Jeff to go out to dinner.

I told Carl that we would be leaving for the night and would be back the next day. Without skipping a beat, Carl responded clearly and painfully, "Oh, that's great. Just time for me to sit around and do nothing." I was surprised at how clearly he expressed what he was feeling, and I knew instantly that we should have stayed with him, but we didn't. During dinner we were feeling regretful as we remembered the exact words that he said. We even wrote them down. I still have that paper and I still get a dull feeling in my stomach when I remember going off and leaving him alone when he was so aware of his need for us to stay with him.

Carl loved classical music and always had it playing softly in his office as he worked. He had the best equipment, which enhanced the sound of the wide variety of musical offerings that he owned. I brought his equipment to Dubuque with us when I took Carl to the nursing home, but I totally neglected to set it up in his room. It never even dawned on me that I should. It was only after he died that I thought about this, and it made me deeply sad. I still feel, deeply, the pain of my thoughtlessness when I let myself remember it. I know that the music would have enlivened his spirit, added greatly to his joy, and enhanced the many idle hours as they passed by.

One night, when Carl was still living at home, I woke up one morning at 1:00 A.M. and found him standing beside my side of the bed. I was shocked to see him there, but quietly got up so as not to frighten him, took him by the hand, and led him back to his side of the bed. Without hesitating he crawled back into bed. I covered him up and went back to my side of the bed, got in, and moved close to him.

After this incident, I was filled with the fear of what might have happened if he had walked out our front door, or the door in the dining room out to the patio. He might have been outside in his pajamas and bare feet not knowing how to get back in. Also, no one might have seen him at that hour of the night. Yet the next day, I didn't do what I should have done: make him an armband with his name, address, and phone number, and change the locks on the doors so he couldn't open them.

Not Accepting the Loss of Memory

Another regret occurred early in our experience with the disease. If Carl didn't remember something I'd tell him that he should have remembered it. I wasn't kind in my response. One time he wanted me to tell him what he had forgotten. I was so irritated with this that I refused to tell him what he had forgotten.

There were times when Carl would lose track of bits and pieces of what he wanted to say. I would try to fill in the blanks but not always patiently. When he would notice my impatience, he would give up. Instead of helping him more, I'd be relieved and tell him that it was okay. Fortunately, as soon as I realized what I was doing, I radically changed my behavior. Yet I've never fully recovered from the regret that I feel about how I acted toward him in those early days when he was losing his memory.

What I learned during those moments of impatience were so instructional that, even to this day, when someone with whom I'm talking is searching for a word or a name I may supply the word or the name. But mostly I simply wait lovingly, not caring at all about the gap or the break. It's usually a temporary loss of memory or totally unimportant.

Denial played a big part in my behavior. Initially, I simply couldn't or wouldn't reckon with the fact that Carl was becoming totally dependent on me for much of his physical and mental care.

One moment particularly haunts me. I had dressed Carl and was buttoning his shirt when I told him how much I hated doing that. His response was, "I'm sorry that I hurt you so much." With utter unkindness I said back, "Sorry doesn't do it." I immediately felt horrible about my response and told him so. We held each other close for a few moments. It was in those moments that I knew that I had to accept the fact that the journey we were on wasn't easy and that it wasn't going to get easier.

There were other times when I lost it but none as unkind as that incident. What was particularly instructional to me during the times when I acted badly is that Carl was always tolerant of my behavior. He accepted me just as I was. Fortunately, I grew in accepting him just as he was.

Those caregiving experiences, more than anything else, still make a difference in my life. I find myself consciously being more accepting of people just as they are. That is one of the greatest gifts that I've received from my role as a caregiver.

Chapter 9
Unforgettable and Precious Moments

Throughout the nine years of caregiving there were some precious and unforgettable times. I don't remember nearly all of them, but these are ones that I will never forget.

I was working in the dining room one morning and Carl was in the living room, close by and sleeping. After a while, I heard him get out of his chair, which wasn't unusual because he had a habit of waking and moving around a bit, then returning to his chair. After a while, however, I didn't hear him moving around and I got up to check on him. He wasn't in the living room, he wasn't upstairs in his office, and he wasn't in the basement.

I panicked and rushed out the front door calling his name. He didn't answer. Then I noticed a car parked at the edge of our driveway, just sitting there. In sheer panic, I approached the car and the lady in it opened the window facing me. I asked her, "Did you happen to see a gentleman walking anywhere?" She asked, "Was he tall? Did he have white hair? Was he wearing a green jacket?" I answered, "Yes, but his jacket is blue." She answered, "I think I saw him on Stafford Street. Do you want to get in and see if we can find him?" I answered, "Oh, please!"

She made a U-turn and drove to Stafford. As we were driving past a lane that turns into a cul-de-sac she slowed so that we could see if he had gone that way. As we approached 16th Street she said, "We'll go left here and if he isn't at the end of this street we'll come back and go right." To my intense relief, Carl was walking at the end of 16th Street, and as soon as I saw him I told her that it was him. She asked if I wanted her to drive both of us back to our house. I replied, "No, we'll be fine." I thanked her profusely and she said, "It's fine. Maybe someday it'll be one of my parents."

I had never seen that car parked at the end of our driveway before nor did I ever see it there again. I kept looking for it to be there again because I wanted to tell her how much her care and generous intervention had meant to me. I firmly believe it was a miracle and I will always be grateful for and in awe of that event.

Another incident happened at a dentist's office near Stonehill, the nursing home where Carl had moved. We had stopped into the office to make an appointment for Carl to have his teeth cleaned. As we waited in the office for the receptionist to see us, I turned the wheelchair so that it faced me and while I talked with Carl. I was doing practically all the talking. But during a pause in the conversation he looked at me and said clearly, lovingly and distinctly, "You are so beautiful." I was utterly surprised; actually, so overwhelmed that I cried, giving expression to the utter joy that I was feeling. It was an unforgettable moment, one that I will always remember.

Unexpected Questions

When individuals are in the last stages of Alzheimer's we may have an unwarranted tendency to believe that they are totally unaware of what is going on around them, totally out of it. Carl proved me wrong on that one several times. Two instances that I remember vividly follow here.

One afternoon Vince Vanden Heuvel and his friend, Lemi Gudeta from Ethiopia, were visiting with Carl. When they were ready to leave, Vince asked Carl if he could take a picture of him with Lemi. Carl looked directly at Vince, and instead of saying "Yes," he asked, "To what purpose?" He waited for an explanation before he agreed to the photo. It was a delightful moment, one that actually brought laughter, and it made us aware that a lot was still going on in Carl's mind.

Another time I was afraid that Carl was forgetting who I was. In a worried and concerned tone, I looked at him and asked, "Carl, what is my name?" When he didn't answer immediately I became a bit frantic and desperately asked, "Carl, what is my name?" He looked at me and with a big grin asked, "Don't you know who you are?" I was so relieved I laughed aloud, and so did he. It was an utterly precious moment!

Two weeks before Carl died, our godson, Miguel, his mother, Leyda Fajardo, and his aunt, Odeth Yalcin, came from Arlington, Virginia to spend time with Carl and me. The day before they arrived, Carl had been put on oxygen. While Miguel, Leyda, and Odeth were visiting, the oxygen line on Carl's left ear fell off onto his shoulder. Miguel noticed, went to Carl, and said, "Carl, I promise this won't hurt but I'm going to put the line back on your ear." After Miguel put the line back on his ear, Carl looked at him and said clearly and gratefully, "Miguelito, I love you." We were all so touched by Carl's words to Miguel that all of us spontaneously hugged him and he hugged us back. It was truly a beautiful moment!

The Gift of Presence

Perhaps one of the best presents I gave to Carl during the last thirteen months of his illness was my presence. Those times were utterly precious to me, as I'm sure they were for Carl.

I was still working a bit, but I was officially retired so I could be with Carl for many hours during every day. His appreciation of my presence was apparent in how he would respond when I'd wheel him into his room after lunch. We had a ritual. I'd brush his teeth, read to him from the Book of Psalms for five minutes or so, then I'd tell him, "Carl I'll be with you all afternoon." A slight grin of joy would suffuse his face and he'd close his eyes to rest a bit. Every once in a while he'd wake up and look to see if I were still there. I always was. I had my laptop with me, a book or a newspaper, some letter-writing materials, and his bed on which I could rest if I chose.

Another part of those days was taking Carl to any events that were planned for the residents, whether in the afternoon or evening. He always had a companion; he was never alone. This was not just a gift for Carl. It was a continuance of our marriage, a continuance of our promise, "for better or for worse," and it fulfilled me as much as I believe it fulfilled him. It was not a sacrifice. It was a joy.

Those times were truly the best of times. I'll always be grateful I not only had the time, but that I took it.

Chapter 9

Chapter 10
Remembering Our Loved One

Our memories hold the stories that make up our lives. Who we have been and who we are is deposited in that storehouse. Our memories also contain the stories of our loved ones, and it is good to remember who our loved ones were when they themselves can no longer remember.

What was Carl like? He was incredibly genteel, quiet, and observant. He respected people just the way they were, whether they were strangers, friends, or family. People tended to trust him with their worries and concerns, and he responded with a caring and gentle wisdom that made a difference.

Carl was unbelievably kind. He possessed a quiet and accepting demeanor that somehow allowed anyone and everyone who was a part of his life to be simply who they were. He placed no expectations on me or on others. He truly enjoyed people just as they were. Carl rarely laughed aloud but he was quick to smile and chuckle when someone did something funny or made a witty remark. He was incredibly humble. He appreciated his gifts, but he didn't think they were greater than anyone else's. He treated others as equals.

Carl's job was writing and preparing presentations for conferences or workshops. He had a ritual that he stuck to every day. After breakfast he would go to his office, meditate for a half hour, then work steadily on the textbooks we were writing, on outlines for presentations, or on sessions for a workshop. Around noon or one o'clock he'd eat lunch, or we'd go out for lunch. After that, he'd go for a walk for half an hour or so. Then he'd return to his office and continue writing until six o'clock. Carl loved to write, and he could do it with relative ease.

He was incredibly professional, which was evident in how serious he was about the invitations we received from parishes and dioceses. Before we would prepare for the sessions he would call the people in charge to find out what expectations they had, what needs they hoped we might meet, and if there were any issues we should be sensitive about. Even if we had done the same presentation at another parish or diocesan event we would prepare anew. Carl's concern and commitment were to meet the unique needs of each place to which we were invited. He felt that to do otherwise might waste their time and ours.

How Carl Dealt with Difficult Issues

Carl and I were constantly working with publishers and editors. Disagreements regarding a manuscript or article would come up on a fairly regular basis. Carl and I would consider every angle of the disagreement, then would let the publisher or editor know if we agreed or disagreed on an issue. If we agreed with their assessment we would comply, but if we didn't we never backed down and always made our position known.

Carl had a style that showed the other person that the change was not only in our favor but also in theirs. In two instances the situation was so serious we needed to speak directly with the publishers. In both instances, necessary changes were made in our favor because Carl was able to negotiate with wisdom and grace.

During his whole adult life, and perhaps before he became an adult, Carl suffered from depression. He took the medication Zoloft every day and that seemed to keep most of the symptoms in control. He wisely saw a psychiatrist on a regular basis, which also helped him deal with the symptoms. Because of his quiet and unassuming nature, hardly anyone but me was aware of this ongoing challenge in his life.

Another serious health issue was difficulty breathing. Because of medication that he took as a child to deal with serious asthma attacks he had only twenty percent of his lung capacity. The medication he took daily helped him live peacefully with that challenge, although it was always a concern for both of us.

Carl handled criticism with amazing acceptance. When I would criticize him, sometimes unkindly, he would simply accept it. He never responded in kind. When criticism would occur in evaluations at a workshop, he totally acknowledged them as probably deserved. He never questioned them. He simply took them in stride. One time I was genuinely upset about a criticism I received during a workshop. He quieted my feelings about the attack by asking, "What will this mean in thirty years?"

What Made Carl Most Happy?

There were two things that made Carl happier than anything else: Being with me, and his godchildren.

Carl enjoyed being with me. This was evident in many ways, particularly in the smile that would cover his face whenever he saw me – anywhere, anytime. This joy continued even while he suffered from Alzheimer's. Surprisingly, he always remembered who I was even when he was close to death, including the Thursday before he died.

He had been placed in hospice care, so I knew that death was near and that I had to write his obituary. I had tried several times before, but I'd end up crying and couldn't finish it. I knew now I didn't have a choice, so I went to my computer and completed a draft. I had finished it shortly before noon, so I went to Stonehill, the nursing home, to be with him for lunch. The aides knew that I would be coming as usual, and they had him waiting at the entrance to his room in his wheelchair. When he saw me he said these unforgettable words, "Oh, there you are; there you are."

Our godchildren, Angela and Miguel, filled Carl with joy and made his life worthwhile. This was evident in many ways. For example, when they were young, they would come to our home after school every day. The moment they arrived Carl would come down from his office to be with them. He would always ask them how their day went and would listen carefully to everything they shared. Sometimes they didn't have much to share, but sometimes they did.

He always told them his thoughts on an issue and listened to theirs. These moments were times when his care of them was evident, and it made a difference in their lives.

One time, during a meeting in our parish, Holy Trinity in Georgetown, we were asked to answer several questions. One of the questions was, "What is the most important thing that you've done in your life?" Carl answered this by saying that co-parenting Angela and Miguel was the most important thing that he had done. At another time, he said what he deeply believed they were the children God had given us.

Carl wasn't one to save things, but he kept a letter from Miguel that made him chuckle every time he read it, which was often. This is that letter.

Dear Carl,

It's hard to know what to say to a godfather. Well a very good one. I want you to know that your I very nice person and very fun to be with. I am so to lucky to have a godfather like you. It's been a pleasure knowing you and always will.

Your God son,

Miguel

PS If you give my ten bucks I'll like you even more! JUST KIDING

Other Joys

Unless we were away during a weekend giving a presentation, a workshop or attending a conference, Carl would spend it with his camera walking around D.C., Virginia, and Maryland taking pictures of whatever captured his attention, interest, and imagination. He was incredibly good at it and was invited to exhibit his photos at galleries in Baltimore and Washington. He also wrote meditations about his photos, and for several years his photo mediations were published in diocesan newspapers. In 1977, seventy of them were published by Thomas More Press in a book titled *Photomeditations*.

Carl loved classical music. He had a Bose disc player in his office and often had pieces playing softly while he worked. He particularly loved violin music. This story about his love for violin music will always remain in my memory. While he was a resident in Stonehill, I made sure that he attended musical and other events. During musical events when the residents would applaud following a piece, Carl never seemed moved enough to join in the applause, so I'd put one of my hands against one of his and we'd applaud together. This changed one afternoon when the lead violinist of the Dubuque Symphony Orchestra came to Stonehill and played for the residents. When she ended a piece and the residents applauded, Carl enthusiastically applauded on his own.

Carl was addicted to great art. Wherever we traveled, both in the United States and abroad, we visited art museums. We were regular visitors at the National Museum of Art and the Smithsonian in Washington while we lived in the East. We were in Amsterdam for the one hundredth anniversary of the death of Vincent Van Gogh and spent hours in the Van Gogh Museum there. When we were in Barcelona we walked around looking at the buildings and artwork of Antoni Gaudí, whose art was found throughout the city. We visited the Louvre in Paris with our goddaughter, Angela, when she was seven years old. Among the many other museums we visited was the Munch Museum in Oslo, where we bought a poster of his work, *The Scream*.

We never bought much other art until Carl came upon a serigraph by John August Swanson in an art shop in San Diego. He loved it and we bought it. Then we bought another and another until we had a collection of six pieces by Swanson: *The Story of Ruth*,

The Classroom, The River, The Nativity, The Story of Joseph and *The Wedding Feast*.

Admittedly I didn't remember specifics about Carl until after his death, but when I did it filled me with joy, helped me deal with the fact that he was no longer with me, and added profoundly to my gratitude for the years that he was in my life.

If the person to whom you are giving care is still alive, I strongly recommend that you take time to remember his or her goodness, to savor how the Divine is continually revealed in him or her and be grateful for the difference he or she makes in your life and the lives of others. Many of those truths are often revealed in an obituary. Don't wait. Remember and celebrate the person now.

Chapter 11
Transitioning to a Nursing Home
or Assisted Living

There may be a time when you can no longer care for your loved one at home. When this occurs an important step to take is to become familiar with assisted living and nursing home facilities in your area. This means visiting them ahead of time, getting information about them from families who have members living in them, and determining which place might be the best fit.

A critical measure is the overall cleanliness of the place, the entrance, the dining area, the kitchen, the recreational spaces, and the bedrooms. An even more important step is to learn about the reputations of the administrator and the staff, especially the nurses and the aides. If possible, spend time with one or more of the residents. Are they content? Are they happy? These are critical steps to take to ensure the safety and care of your loved one.

Once you have chosen a nursing home or assisted living facility and have been accepted, the next step is moving your loved one. For some time now, you have probably struggled with caring for him or her and have come to the realization that you no longer have the emotional or physical strength to continue. This is often a very difficult decision to make but it is necessary for the protection and safety of the person with Alzheimer's.

In addition to being a difficult decision, the move itself is often painful both for the person with Alzheimer's and the caregiver. I remember vividly the day I took Carl to Stonehill, the nursing home we chose for him. He knew to some extent what was happening because every step of the way I told him what we were doing. He cooperated fully until it was time for me to go home. He simply couldn't understand why I wasn't taking him with me. He exhibited a real need to continue being together. I finally convinced him that I had to go, and he let me go. The separation hurt so badly that I cried all the way home.

The next day I ate a hurried breakfast and returned to the nursing home to be with Carl. He was so glad to see me that the pain of the decision hit me all over again. Mysteriously, during those moments, I realized that mentally he was severely diminished but emotionally he was well enough. I also sensed that, even though I was no longer able to care for him physically, I needed to continue caring for him emotionally. I needed to be a presence, an anchor. I realized, too, that *I* needed to be with him.

During that first morning he didn't resist the food, but he didn't eat much of it. I told the staff that his favorite breakfast was Cheerios with a banana, blueberries, almonds, walnuts, and skim milk. I also told them that he liked his coffee hot. They told me that would not be a problem, and asked if he would be satisfied with pancakes, bacon, and eggs on the weekend. I was sure that would be fine.

That intervention made me aware of how important it is to do everything that we can to make sure our loved one is able to continue enjoying the things they like and are used to. I found the staff not only open to my suggestions but eager to do whatever they could to make Carl feel welcome and at home.

Meeting the Needs of the Person with Alzheimer's
As soon as I realized that breakfast would go smoothly I decided to delay going to the nursing home until lunchtime. I purchased lunch so that I was able to eat with Carl. He was normally a slow eater and I wasn't in any hurry, so the arrangement worked out perfectly.

Fortunately, I was retired so I could also spend the afternoon with him. One of the things that we did almost every afternoon was go outside for a half hour or more walk. He enjoyed this because it was something we had done together at home. We walked hand-in-hand, which provided support for both of us.

Carl tended to be cold no matter what time of year it was. He needed a sweater and a warm outer garment. I made this need known to the aides and nurses, and the need was almost always met. I also made sure, when I was with him, that he was comfortable.

Carl loved visitors. He was used to his godchildren and/or their dad or mom being with us almost every day. He was also used to frequent dinners with friends both in our home and in theirs. He loved it when people dropped in, no matter the time or day. It didn't matter that he couldn't necessarily converse very well. He simply enjoyed the "being with." We made friends fairly quickly when we moved to Dubuque, and they often stopped to visit. They enjoyed being with Carl as much as he enjoyed their presence.

Another thing that was important to Carl was touch. Holding hands was something that we always did. We continued doing that. Hugging was always part of how family and friends greeted both him and me when we got together. That continued in the nursing home. I kissed him every day, both when I arrived and before I left, sometimes more than once. Often when we were watching television together, I'd move my chair close to his chair and lean my arm comfortably and lovingly against his. During the nursing home experience, I learned how vital touch is. More than anything else it continues to unite.

Carl had always enjoyed going out for lunch or dinner. For several months after I took him to Stonehill we frequently went out to local restaurants in Dubuque until he had difficulty knowing how to get into the car. Over time, he totally resisted our efforts to help him.

Religious services were always important to us and we were able to continue participating in them at the nursing home. Every Sunday we joined the community at Mass and were always able to sit in the same seats, which was comforting for Carl and for me.

Owning Our Own Uniqueness

Each person with Alzheimer's is unique – just as each one of us is unique. The way Carl behaved with this disease may not be the way your relative or friend behaves. What is critical and vitally important is to appreciate what is unique in them, and respect what he or she needs for happiness, contentment, and peace. Also important is that you do everything you can to assure that life in the nursing home is as good as it can be.

The most important thing that I learned in my caregiving journey with Carl, especially during the thirteen months that he was in the nursing home, is that he needed *me*. I believe, deeply, that being with him as much as was possible made a profoundly gracious difference in the last chapter of his life. It also made a difference in mine.

Two friends, whose mothers were in the same nursing home as Carl, shared their experiences of what I've described above.

Joani McKay

I know how it feels to leave a visit with your person and know that you made their day. When my mom was at Stonehill, I remember many a day I would walk in there with having had a stressful day teaching and would leave feeling soooo good. My mom lost her ability to communicate with me, but I always got a smile, as she knew I belonged to her.

Donna Wahlert

I learned more about living in the present and letting things flow every time I visited my mom at Stonehill. She was in a different world and I joined her there. We lived entirely in the present. The past had peeled away, and she couldn't think of a future. When I joined her where she was, it was a relief.

Your own well-being is as important as the well-being of the person with Alzheimer's. Following the placement of your loved one in the nursing home, if you need to get your own life in order, take the time that you need to do so. It may mean taking a vacation or simply getting rest. Find someone else to keep in touch with both the nursing home and your relative during the time that you're taking a break.

I don't regret a single thing that I did with Carl, but I didn't do what I suggest above. I became totally drained and ended up in the hospital. Actually, I almost died. I would not want that to happen to any other caregiver. To give less, at times, can sometimes mean giving more in the long run. What is vitally important is to give what you can in terms of your personal situation and needs, but to also be keenly aware of your limits.

Chapter 12
Becoming an Advocate

For me, becoming an advocate was never planned. It happened in unexpected moments and often was a surprise when it occurred.

My goddaughter, Angela, was with Carl and me when I took him from our home in Arlington, Virginia to Stonehill, in Dubuque. When we departed from the Washington airport our carry-ons were put in a cargo area on the plane. When we arrived at O'Hare in Chicago and got off the plane we had to wait near the exit door for our carry-ons to be delivered. A wheelchair was also waiting for us at the exit door. We expected that Carl would simply sit in the wheelchair, but he wouldn't. He simply didn't understand that this was what he was supposed to do.

The gentleman who was in charge of the wheelchair tried everything he knew to get him to sit in it, but nothing worked. Angela and I tried to help him sit down but he simply stood there, rigidly. I noticed while we were trying to get Carl to sit in the wheelchair that others who were waiting for their carry-ons were watching with curiosity and interest. Finally, we were able to get Carl to sit in the wheelchair and when he did, those who were watching us clapped. I understood because I felt like clapping, too. I looked at them, smiled, and said protectively, almost proudly, "He has Alzheimer's!" A look of kindness and appreciation was the group's response, and with a show of respect, they waited until we had our carry-ons and then stood aside to let us pass.

Carl and I were parishioners at a parish in Washington, D.C. Over time, it became apparent that when we approached the eucharistic minister to receive the Eucharist, it took Carl a while to know what to do. This was discomforting for the minister and for those who were behind us. Then one Sunday we were visiting at another parish in South Arlington, Virginia. I was worried about what would happen at Communion time. When we approached the altar, however, the pastor, Father Leonard Tuozzolo, immediately sensed Carl's hesitation and lovingly guided Carl to hold out his hand to receive the host and place it in his mouth. It was an utterly sacred moment. It was also the moment I knew Our Lady Queen of Peace was the parish where we would celebrate the Eucharist from then on.

An Incident in the Nursing Home

I was nearly always with Carl for both his noon and evening meals. One Sunday, our friends Bernie and Phyllis Curran, from Galena, Illinois, invited me to go with them to look at homes in Dubuque, where they were planning to move. I told them, "Yes" but I wanted to be with Carl for lunch. As soon as lunch was finished, I left the table expecting that an aide would take Carl back to his room.

At 4:30 I asked Bernie and Phyllis to return me to the nursing home because I wanted to be with Carl for the evening meal. When I arrived in Carl's room he seemingly wasn't there. I went to the front desk and asked the nurse in charge where Carl was. She asked, "Isn't he in his room?" I answered, "He's not in his chair." She quickly sent someone down the wing to check, which I thought was strange, because Carl was no longer able to get around on his own.

I returned to his room and because I needed to go to the bathroom I stepped into his. Carl was sitting on the stool and the look on his face was one of pure relief, almost joy, when he saw me. I realized that he had been sitting on the stool since the aide had returned him to his room following lunch. She had obviously put him on the stool, tended to another individual, forgot about Carl, and then left because her shift was over.

I was so shocked I could hardly breathe but I got him up, pulled up his pants, hugged him, put him in his chair, talked with him quietly and waited for an aide to wheel him into the dining room for the evening meal. I didn't say anything to the aide nor the nurse at the desk because I was afraid that what I might say would be out of outrage, disbelief, and anger. After dinner I went back with him to his room and stayed with him for another hour. Then I drove home, crying all the way.

I couldn't sleep so I got up and wrote a letter to the administrator describing, in detail, the situation, which I gave to her the next day. The following is the letter that I wrote:

3/11, 2007

Regarding Carl Pfeifer, by Janaan Manternach

With the greatest respect for everyone who is on staff on Second Floor, I need to address a care issue that occurred this afternoon.

I fed Carl his lunch and left the dining room at 1:10 to go to lunch with friends. I returned at 4:50. Carl was not in his chair in his room nor was he sitting in the dining room or near the nurse's station. I asked the nurse in charge where Carl was, and she immediately sent an aide to look for him. The aide went from room to room in his wing, which kind of puzzled me because Carl, unable to walk independently, couldn't have wandered on his own into another room.

While she was doing that I decided to use Carl's bathroom, and when I pulled the curtain back he was sitting on the stool with his pants around his ankles, partially unclothed. I was shocked to see him there as was the aide who had been looking for him.

She told me that when the second shift came on duty they were told that Carl and I had gone out. I'm worried about that information because I couldn't have taken him out of the building without help and I would never have taken him without specifically telling the charge nurse that I was doing that and where I was taking him. Furthermore, the aides who took him to the bathroom would have had to complete that duty before I could have taken him out.

What disturbs me greatly and really makes me sad is that I suspect Carl sat on the stool partially unclothed for perhaps more than two and a half hours. I'm also gravely concerned that he could have tried to get up, tripped on his pants, fallen, and hurt himself. A further concern is that no one might have heard him fall.

He could have lain on the floor until I returned. Also, if I had not returned, which could have likely happened, how long might Carl have continued sitting in the bathroom? Would he have missed dinner? Not have been put to bed?

Because I suspect this was a most unusual oversight, I can totally forgive it, but I hope and pray that nothing like this will ever happen again to Carl nor to anyone else. The reason that I believe that it was unusual is because the aides – all of them – are genuinely kind and caring to him. Carl is always happy when he sees them, and I know that he trusts them.

Perhaps this is also a good time to mention that because Carl is so quiet I worry that he, at times, sits unattended for too long after meals and following activities. That, however, is a minor concern compared to the above.

The Administrator was taken aback and checked into the situation. The aide suggested that she thought I had taken Carl out with me. As I noted in my letter, however, I would have had to check him out before doing that and his name was not listed as "out." The administrator set up a meeting with me and another person on the staff. They apologized profusely, told me what action had been taken with the aide, and suggested that it was the first time that such a situation had occurred.

I believed them, but I still often wonder what would have happened if I had not returned when I did. Would anyone have checked on him? How long would he have continued to sit on the stool? Could the situation have turned into a tragedy? I'm hoping that the advocacy that I did for Carl in that situation assured that it never did happen again.

Continuing to Advocate

Another instance in which I was an advocate on Carl's behalf happened in relationship to a room change. Individuals' names were on a list for rooms with a private bathroom when they became available on one of the wings. I was aware that Carl's name had gotten to first place on the list and that one was going to be available. I also heard rumors that someone else was going to get the room, someone who had more clout than Carl.

I was determined that Carl would get the room, so I wrote a strong, no-nonsense letter to the administrator in which I stated the rule in place at the nursing home in such situations and made it clear that it would be immoral, unjust, and unfair to give the room to someone else. Carl got the room!

I feel I would be remiss if I were not to add that I never needed to be an advocate for Carl again at Stonehill. On a monthly basis, I could let the staff know how I felt about the care he was receiving or if there was anything that I wanted added or changed. The nurses and aides were always respectful and kind. This was evident when a staff member would stop in his room to check on him. His face would light up because he liked the staff and knew that they cared about him.

I will always be grateful to Stonehill for making the last months of Carl's life peaceful, comfortable, and caring. He could not have been in a better place.

That being said, the challenge of being an advocate is a very real and critical one in the care of someone who cannot stand up for him or herself. It takes attention to what is happening in the day-to-day care and the courage to act when the treatment is not what the person with Alzheimer's deserves and should expect. It is one of the best reasons why it is vitally important to be with your loved one, if not every day, as often as you can be.

Chapter 13
Preparing for the End of Life

Long-term care insurance is important to consider long before it may become necessary. Carl and I had no idea we would ever need it, but when we were introduced by a friend to a financial planner she told us that she wouldn't take us on as clients unless we signed up for long-term care insurance. We agreed, and fortunately, it was a good thing we did.

We didn't have the most expensive plan, and when Carl had to go into the nursing home I had to pay for the first one hundred days, which amounted to approximately $16,000. But for the rest of the time he was in there our long-term care insurance paid the monthly fee.

Because of that experience I strongly recommend looking into long-term care insurance. If you don't want to go that route, it's wise, I believe, to look into what may be available if and when there is a need for assisted living or nursing home care, such as Medicaid and/or Title 19 funds.

If you already have a Last Will and Testament or a Trust Agreement in place you may want to go over it to make changes, and bring it up-to-date. If you don't have either, now might be a good time to contact a lawyer for help, or draw up your own version and have it certified. I go over mine yearly and surprisingly, there are always some additions or deletions that I want or need to make.

Writing an Obituary
Consider writing an obituary while the person is still alive. This task may seem ghoulish and you may not want to do it. Admittedly,

I didn't write Carl's until three days before he died, although I had tried to write it earlier. The good thing about writing it in advance is that you can keep adding to it as new thoughts arise about who your loved one is and was. This is the one that I wrote about Carl.

Carl J. Pfeifer

Carl J. Pfeifer, 78, of 1045 Rockdale Rd. Dubuque, formerly of 1620 N. Quebec Street, Arlington, Va., died of Alzheimers at 1:05 a.m., Thursday, July 12, 2007, at Stonehill Care Center.

His body was donated to the Deeded Body Program at the University of Iowa College of Medicine. A Memorial Mass will be celebrated at St. Martin's Catholic Church in Cascade, at 10 a.m. on July 28, 2007, with Rev. Neil J. Manternach officiating. Concelebrating is Rev. Douglas Loecke, Rev. Msgr. Albert Manternach and Rev. Carl J. Manternach. Eulogy will be given by Angela Barbieri. Relatives and friends may call after 9 a.m. at the church. The Reiff Funeral Home in Cascade is in charge of arrangements.

He was born on June 22, 1929, in St. Louis, Mo., son of Carl and Emma (Heine) Pfeifer. He was a member of the Society of Jesus, Missouri Province, for 29 years. On Nov. 20, 1976, he married Janaan Manternach, a former Dubuque Franciscan at Holy Trinity Church in Georgetown, DC.

Carl was a prolific writer of religion textbooks, and single title books on catechetics, theology, prayer, meditation, and the saints. He also wrote numerous articles for journals, newspapers, and newsletters. He co-authored with his wife the trend setting religion series, "LIFE, LOVE, JOY." It dramatically changed how Catholic children are taught religion.

He was widely known as a lecturer on catechetics and religious education throughout the United States, Europe, Canada, Guam, and Central America. He taught summer sessions at both the Catholic University of America, and St. Michael's College in Winooski, Vermont. He also taught courses at Theological College in Washington, D.C., and St. Mary's Seminary and University in Baltimore, Md.

Carl and his wife, Janaan, were presented the prestigious annual award from the National Conference of Catechetical Leadership recognizing their long and illustrious contribution to catechetical ministry. They were the first married couple to receive this award. They were also honored by the National Association of Parish Catechetical Directors with the Emmaus Award for Excellence in Catechesis. This award was given to them because of their international reputation and contribution to the field of Catholic catechesis through writing, publishing and teaching.

He was an avid photographer. For several years, he wrote a weekly photo- meditation, which appeared in many Diocesan newspapers. They also became a book titled "Photomeditations" His photos were exhibited in galleries in Washington, D.C., and Baltimore, Md. He was a pioneer in introducing photos of everyday life experience into religion textbooks.

Carl is survived by his wife, Janaan; his brother, Richard (Rosemary) Pfeifer; three brothers-in-law, Thomas (Helen) Manternach, Donald (Anita) Manternach, and Richard Ripple; two sisters-in-law, Grace Miller and Janice Manternach; four godchildren, Angela Barbieri, Miguel Barbieri, Edward Jeep and Emily Jeep Klingaman; two honorary grandchildren, Jake and Hannah Verrips; numerous nieces and nephews including a special nephew, Carl Gerard (Jerry) Pfeifer and his wife, Charlene, who loved their uncle Carl in many simple and cherishing ways.

He was preceded in death by his parents, his father and mother-in-law, Jacob and Anita Takes Manternach; three sisters-in-laws, Janet Manternach Ripple, Luann Vaske Manternach and Cecelia Lucas Manternach; two brothers-in-law, Orland (Bub) Manternach and Donald Jacob Manternach (in infancy); a niece, Amy Manternach Kurt and a niece-in-law, Cathy Kimm Manternach.

Memorials may be given in his name to Stonehill Care Center, the Missouri Province Jesuits (St. Louis), the Sisters of St. Francis (Dubuque, IA), Hospice of Dubuque or to a charity of your choice.

Online condolences may be left for the family at ww.reifffuneralhomeinc.com.

Telegraph Herald
Date of Obituary: July 15, 2007
Dubuque, Iowa

Choosing a Funeral Home

Carl and I had agreed that we would be buried in Cascade, Iowa, my hometown, beside my parents. Actually, my mother had purchased a plot that we were free to use, if we chose.

I contacted the funeral director in Cascade and made the initial arrangements, and when Carl was near death, he came to the nursing home and we finalized them.

One of the decisions Carl and I had made was that after we died we would donate our bodies for use in medical research if they were viable. I chose the University of Iowa Health Care and did all the necessary paperwork. On the day of Carl's death his body was transported to the hospital by the funeral director.

The research took over a year. When it was completed, Carl's body was cremated and his cremains were sent to the funeral director. Below is the letter that I received from the Program Director at University of Iowa Health Care.

Carl's cremains were buried in the plot my mother had given us. Shortly thereafter a beautiful tombstone was created and installed in Calvary Cemetery in Cascade, Iowa. I will also be buried there.

Chapter 14
Memorial Services:
Celebrations of Death and Life

It is not uncommon for people to request no services upon their deaths. Usually, families honor their wishes. I went all out, however, to memorialize and celebrate Carl's life. I had a brief service at the nursing home the morning Carl died so that immediate family members and close friends could view his body and say good-bye before he was transported to the university in Iowa City for research.

Shortly after his death I also arranged for a Memorial Mass at St. Matthias Church in Cascade, Iowa. A month later I had another Memorial Mass in Arlington, Virginia, where we had lived during most of our professional lives. The Masses were similar. The funeral directors in each place, along with relatives and friends, were very helpful in putting the services together.

Tradition dictates a lot of what takes place during these events so not a lot of planning has to occur beforehand. One of the most memorable parts of the Memorial Masses for Carl was the eulogy that was written and lovingly given by our goddaughter, Angela Barbieri Usas, a tribute to her godfather.

Angela's Eulogy

I don't remember when I first learned to say Carl's name because I have known him for that long. Because I adored him so, I wouldn't be surprised if his name was one of the first words I uttered. Carl is a man like no other and that is what makes this celebration both incredibly special and incredibly hard.

I am proud to stand here today as Janaan and Carl's goddaughter. Thanks to Janaan, I am confident most of you know that I am

Angela, because it seems everyone knows that, no matter where I go. I was fortunate, really. I had no say in the matter of selecting my godparents and yet I couldn't have hand-picked a better pair. Today, I am going to talk about one of my godparents, my godfather, Carl. I want to share the impact of his life on mine, for it has been amazing. Carl, Carlos, Carlitos, my dear, dear godfather, was one of the greatest blessings in my life.

Carl was a man of symbolism. He took pictures of nature and objects that were symbolic. He used these pictures in books to add images to his work. Carl also used symbols and pictures for personal enjoyment. If any of you have been to an event with Carl, you are a witness that he took pictures! He was so good at taking pictures because unlike most, Carl paid attention to detail. He had an uncanny way of finding symbols and meaning in daily objects, people and places. He captured practically all of my brother's and my childhood moments on film. They truly are a priceless gift.

Back to symbolism. Carl's most important symbol was his wedding band. I am not sure how many of you ever noticed Janaan and Carl's wedding rings, but they are gold bands with three words engraved on them: Life, Love, Joy. The words made up the title of the first CCD (Confraternity of Christian Doctrine) curriculum Janaan and Carl wrote together.

In Carl's last weeks, I found myself thinking about a man I loved: who he was and all that he meant to me and my family. Those words kept resurfacing: Life, Love, Joy. To give tribute to my godfather, I have based my eulogy around them.

Life
What a life Carl lived, and through his living, we all benefited. Carl was a holy man, so spiritual and selfless. Very few people listen the way Carl listened, and that is because he knew the importance of being present in every moment. I was the opposite of Carl, but I have been learning through Carl's example. Many go through life worrying about what's next and not paying attention to the now. Not Carlos. When he came downstairs in the afternoons when Miguel and I were over, he was with us. He listened to our unending reports of our school day, helped us on whatever homework was due, and drove us to whatever events we had.

Carl was the most disciplined man I have ever met. My brother, Miguel, and I would test him on it constantly. What most amazed us as children was that we would tempt Carlos with cookies, pastries, or Janaan's freshly made popcorn and he would always decline. If Miguel and I were to ask him why, he would simply say that he only ate at meal times. His response never passed judgment, but showed integrity in following what he believed in.

Carl also moved through life at his own pace. The term "hurry up" did not apply. Carl was never in a rush because that would force him to potentially miss a very important detail in the day. Carl loved his daily walks around the neighborhood! He would look at everything he passed, and he befriended the squirrels outside his and Janaan's house (much to Janaan's dislike). With a handful of peanuts, he would call out, "here squirrelly" and as intently as he gave his attention to humans, he shared the same respect for animals and the nature around him.

Love
The second, and possibly, most important word on Carl's and Janaan's wedding band is "love." I am pretty sure we would all agree that we have never known a love like Janaan's and Carl's. In our family we nicknamed them "C&J." We had to abbreviate it really, because they were always together. In fact, the only times I can recall C&J *not* being together was when Janaan had lunch with Susan Keys, Maureen Riddel, or Kathy Fredgren.

What that really means is that Janaan and Carl lived together, worked together, and did everything else together. For example, if they were out of milk, or blueberries, bananas, or cereal they both went to the grocery store to get it. A special part of C&J's daily schedule frequently included an outing for lunch. They often went to the Metro 29 diner, one of Carl's favorites. The idea for going there was Carl's. He said it was a good time to get to know who we were living with.

I guess what stands out to me the most about C&J's love is that it seemed so easy. They obviously enjoyed one another's company. They never tired of being together. I have always admired their love and relationship.

Carl not only shared his love with Janaan. He had an immense amount of love to share with those surrounding him. C&J never had children of their own. Recently Janaan shared with me that Carl called Mig and me "the children God gave us." What an honor. My parents are really to be thanked for sharing us and allowing us to have four caring adults instead of two. It certainly was a gift for Miguel and me.

While Carl was known as my godfather he was much, much more than that. Carl went well beyond the definition of "godfather," as he was a constant presence. My family, with C&J, shared countless meals together at least once a week, usually more. Meals were special because many hands went into preparing it, and good conversations always accompanied the food.

Another special tradition with Carl was when we went to Southern Shores in the Outer Banks. Here we celebrated Miguel's and my birthdays. C&J always made a slideshow of our growth throughout the year, accompanied by the song, "I Am A Promise." It took a lot of work, considering that seventy slides had to synchronize with the lyrics, but they always did an incredible job.

Finally, a favorite tradition that I will carry on with my children is our celebration of St. Nick. Every December 6, we'd have dinner at C&J's. The anticipation and thrill were just like Christmas. For years, Miguel and I would await the nuts, tangerines, and Snickers that he brought us. (Pause.) Miguel was the one to discover that "St. Nick" was actually Carlos. He crept downstairs to surprise Carl as he tried to sneak back into the house. You should have seen the tears of laughter we all had! We continued to celebrate the holiday, always remembering that special December 6.

I could go on and on. My point is that Carl was around for all the big steps and the little steps I made in life. He always supported me. He did his best to guide me, while giving me space to be myself and make my own decisions. Carl loved me unconditionally. I knew it and I am grateful.

Joy
The last word on the ring is joy. The joy that Carl gave to each one of us is what has led us to gather and celebrate him today. It was a joy to have known Carl. A joy to have connected with him in whatever ways each of us did. And it will remain a joy to think of the man he was and how he touched our lives.

There is one more story I have to share that brings me continued joy and strength in moving forward from today. On different occasions in the last few months of Carl's life, Janaan asked him for his ring for fear that something might happen to it. He would either grunt, "Mm-mm" or simply fold his hand together, forming a fist so the ring could not be taken off. Even in the last week, Janaan asked him for the ring, yet he would not be without it. While this concerned Janaan, it was also a comfort that Carl died wearing his wedding band.

Janaan had called me at 1:30 A.M. to tell me that Carl had died, but it didn't really register until 10:00 A.M. that morning. At that time, I called Janaan, sobbing. I asked if she had gotten Carl's ring. I don't know why I was so worried to make sure that she had it, but I was. Ironically, after several attempts, two dear friends, Phyllis and Bernie Curran, had just gotten Carl's ring off five minutes before I called. Janaan was sitting in relief that she had Carl's ring and then I called asking about it.

I arrived in Iowa two weeks ago and Janaan gave me Carl's most treasured possession. I have been wearing it ever since and have felt a great sense of joy when I see it because it reminds me of Carl. Janaan says that no matter where I go now, Carl will be holding my hand. I agree and find great comfort in that. I also enjoy seeing those three words throughout the day: Life, Love, Joy.

Carl, Carlos, Carlitos, I am grateful that your mind and body are finally at peace. I just ask that you keep your spirit alive in all of us, so that we may be God-filled and continue to live by your example. Amen.

Other Words of Remembrance

Below are a few other words of remembrance that were given at the end of the Liturgy.

By Neil Parent

In 1993, at its annual conference in Pasadena, California, the National Conference for Catechetical Leadership honored Carl and Janaan for their outstanding contribution to catechesis throughout their long careers. In accepting the award, Carl approached the microphone first and began with these words:

"Janaan and I are thrilled and honored to accept this award because we have known so many of you for so long and because of the part we played in NCCL's beginnings. We want to express our thanks (and here there was a noticeable wink), each in our own way."

Carl then proceeded to identify individuals and groups of people who were instrumental in his and Janaan's early formation, beginning with their respective parents. He went on to outline their careers and those who greatly influenced them as religious educators. He also noted their work with the publishing houses of Twenty-Third Publications and Silver Burdett Ginn. I can say that in his remarks, Carl identified, by name, many of you who are in this church today, including at the altar.

Eventually, Carl turned his attention to the home front and to his and Janaan's beloved godchildren, Angela and Miguel. He said, "We are proud to be their *padrinos, compadres* with their parents." He also gave Angela's and Miguel's ages at the time, but we won't disclose them here.

Finally, Carl concluded his remarks by saying this:

"Lastly, we are most grateful to each other, Janaan and I. Alone neither of us could have done what we have done together. I've tried for years to share with Janaan the value of logic, reason, outlines, linear thinking, and all such left-brain skills. She has thrust on me the greater worth of feeling, empathy, circular thought, intuition, poetry, and all the other right-brain gifts. I think I have gained more in the process, as Janaan will now demonstrate."

Before we turn our attention to what Janaan demonstrated, I think it would be good to look closely at Carl's concluding paragraph because it reveals so much about him.

His self-deprecating humor, his humility, his unpretentiousness, his indebtedness to and deep affection for Janaan, not only as his wife but also as his teacher, his understanding of the holistic nature of teaching the faith, that it involves the logical and the intuitive, the linear and, as Angela noted earlier, the symbolic, his exemplifying that to be a good teacher one must first be a good learner – and Carl was an exceptional one. He had made a lifetime commitment to learning. He was never too old or too knowledgeable to learn. Many times I saw Carl attend learning sessions that I knew he could have given with greater experience and knowledge of the subject matter than the presenter. But he was always the learner, seeking to gain some new insight.

Janaan then approached the microphone. I will only give you a glimpse of what she said by reciting the first few lines of her remarks:

> When to us, something happens
> For better or worse
> I'm consciously driven
> To create a verse
> So, these words of acceptance
> A verse-form employs.
> You're in luck we're not singing
> To shout out our joy.
> It's a poem with a story
> A story come true
> That of being awarded
> And chosen by you.

Janaan continued her verse, describing her and Carl's joyous reactions and that of their godchildren, Angela and Miguel, to the award. She also thanked various groups of people, especially the awarding committee. Then she said this:

> There are two more to thank,
> Two biggies for me.
> God, first, and then, Carl.
> Love's a sweet mystery.

Janaan's juxtaposing of God, Carl, love, and mystery in those last two lines sums up, for those of us who knew him, a lot about Carl.

We don't doubt for a second that God's wondrous love shone through Carl as husband, godfather, teacher, relative, friend, colleague, and Christian. Indeed, one of life's great mysteries, if not the core mystery, is that each one of us bears a spark of the Divine flame. Carl modeled for us how to keep our spark burning brightly. May he now continue to inspire us from heaven.

By Jean Marie Heisberger

I'm Jean Marie Heisberger, and my husband, Bob Heyer, and I consider ourselves to be Carl and Janaan's best friends. I'm well aware, however, that about a hundred other people claim the same honor because that's how Carl and Janaan make everyone feel – as though they were their best friends. I feel honored to say a few words about Carl. My real honor, however, is having had the privilege of being not just one of his editors for many years, but having Carl consider me "friend."

Many of us share the opinion that the first descriptive of Carl is that he was a gentleman – a gentleman in the classic meaning of the word but also a gentle man. The most excited I ever saw Carl was to hear him give his little chuckle and quietly say, "Wow, Jean Marie."

Being gentle, however, did not mean Carl didn't have strong opinions. He also had enough German stubbornness to occasionally require "negotiation" about something he wrote. But it was always a very interesting and enlightening discussion, not a battle over who or what was right. Then, when I would acquiesce in such a discussion, (which I frequently did) he'd give me that wonderful little smile of his.

One of the things I admired about Carl was his confident clarity about who he was. This gave him a deep integrity and not an ounce of pretension. Though he knew who he was, Carl was consistently astonished at who other people thought he was. His humility was as genuine as everything else about him. Carl and Janaan's reputation was of having great talent in their profession, yet when I'd invite them to write a First Communion program or a newsletter column (as they both did for many years) they'd seem surprised and genuinely honored to be asked. I am confident that today Carl is astonished at this gathering here, as well as the one we celebrated last month in Iowa.

One more thing I'd like to mention is how Carl shared Janaan's love for children. For our daughter, Kristin's, life markers, he and Janaan faithfully and joyfully traveled – to New Jersey for First Communion, Providence for college graduation, Kansas City for her wedding, and many other occasions. They eagerly tracked every step of her life with loving interest. And Kristin is one of many young people they treated with love and generosity as though they were the only one in Carl and Janaan's life.

So Carl, my friend, for all you were, all you did and all the many people whose lives you touched in your too-brief time with us, all I can say is, "Wow, Carl!"

Words by Carl's Brother, Richard Pfeifer,
Which Were Delivered by His Son, Chris

Carl and I grew up together living upstairs of the bakery on Kings Highway in St. Louis, Missouri. We were always close to each other, playing bottle caps in the back yard, Indian ball in the alley, ash pit hunting, and all the other wonderful things kids did in the good old days. One of our favorite things, in the hot days of summer, was waiting for the milkman or iceman so we could get a handful of ice.

We went to Blessed Sacrament for grade school. Both of us were altar boys. The good sisters were aware of the fact that the bakery was right cross the street and our dad was up early, so somehow we always got to serve the early Masses.

I will always remember Carl saying Mass in our bedroom and me, of course, being the altar boy. I remember his entering the Jesuits, his studies, his ordination, his travels, his marriage, his visits to St. Louis, and eating at our favorite restaurant, Busch's Grove, his taking pictures of everything and everyone, especially the St. Louis Arch, and our children, his quietness, gentleness, kindness, inner strength, and his love of life and family, especially his life with Janaan.

Even though he wore many hats and earned degrees, awards, and titles, I will always remember him as my brother.

Memorials are sacred moments. I believe that the memorials celebrating Carl were one of the best things that I did for him. Friends and relatives had an opportunity to remember, to share, to pray, and to bring closure. It also helped me to let go and say, "Goodbye."

Chapter 15
What I Would Do Now

Here are some things that I would do now if I had the privilege of being a caregiver again.

1. Hydration.
I often drank water during the day to stay hydrated, but I never thought of asking Carl if he were thirsty or would like a glass of water. I would now!

2. Retirement.
I wasn't retired when I became a caregiver and I didn't retire for a while. Now I would retire immediately to be more present to Carl in his aloneness.

3. Support groups.
I did not attend talks or workshops about Alzheimer's nor did I seek help or comfort from support groups. I know now that talking with other caregivers can make a big difference. I would go now!

4. Prayer.
Carl had a ritual before he started work. He would pray by sitting quietly in meditation for 10-15 minutes. Then he would read from the Psalms for another ten minutes. Then he'd reflect for another five minutes on one of his photo meditations or on a saint. He had a Bible, a book of saints, and his book, *Photomediations*, on his desk. I realize now that I could and should have continued that ritual with him. I would now!

5. Death.

Carl was afraid of death. One of his photo meditations, titled "One Way," shows tombstones in the photo. He wrote, "Death is a one-way path ... from which there is no return ... the shadows surrounding the tombstones ... find a resonance in my deepest fears of dying ... I do not want to die."

There were times when I could have talked with him about his fears, especially on June 22, 2007, his birthday. After the guests who had celebrated with us had left, we were waiting for an aide to take him back to his room. I noticed that he looked really sad. I also suspected that he knew it wouldn't be long before his death, which occurred twenty days later on July 12, 2007. I know now that I should have talked with him about death, but I didn't because I, too, am afraid of death. He would have been comforted and I could have assured him that I would be with him. Sadly, I didn't, but I would now!

6. Taking time.

Gradually I noticed that Carl was slower and more challenged at doing things that he normally did with ease. I tended to urge him to do them at his usual pace, not realizing that he couldn't. Actually, sometimes I'd do it for him, which fortunately didn't irk him but it did surprise him. I realize now that I should have totally supported what was going on by letting him do what he *could* do and *wanted* to do at his own pace, and as long as he was able. There really was no need to hurry, and I should have totally given him the time that he needed. I believe it would have made him feel better about himself. I definitely would be more patient now.

7. Kindness.

I was mostly kind to Carl but not always. Unlike what happens in many caregiving-Alzheimer's relationships, Carl was always kind to me. What I would do now if I had the privilege of doing it all over again is that I would always be kind. This means I would totally appreciate how hard the changes in doing things and relating to others are for the person suffering from the disease, and I would love him or her unconditionally no matter how challenging that might be.

8. Writing.

I'm a writer, yet never once during my caregiving years did I take time to write about what was happening as both Carl's and my lives were changing. If I had documented what was going on, I would have more to share in this book, but I didn't. I would now, and I strongly recommend doing it.

9. Rest and self-care.

During the several of the years of caregiving I was always tired, especially after I found Carl standing by my side of the bed one morning at 1 A.M. After that I experienced poor sleeping habits, awakening frequently to make sure he was still in bed. Sometimes I couldn't get back to sleep, so I typically slept less than six hours a night rather than the necessary seven or eight. I was also afraid to take naps during the day because of the possibility that he might wander outside while I was sleeping – which he did at times, even when I was awake.

I was totally unconscious of how important it is to find ways to rest and simply accepted being tired as part of the caregiving challenge. If I had to do it all over again, I would find ways to get the needed rest. It's a critical step in self-care.

10. God's constant care.

I've always had a deep and abiding belief in God, partly because I was reared by deeply religious parents. However, my faith was more along the lines of God seeing everything I was doing, especially the bad stuff. That changed radically during most of my adult years. Yet during my caregiving years I didn't have an abiding and conscious sense that the help which came from a phone call, a visit from a relative or friend with a meal in hand, insight into how to handle a new change in Carl's behavior, invitations to dinner or lunch, or offers to spend time with him that freed me up to do what I needed to do were purely and simply God taking care of both of us.

It is only since I'm no longer a caregiver that I have grown keenly aware of God's loving presence with and for me, making the needed difference that helped me not only survive, but to be mostly loving and gracious. It's never too late to realize that God is with us in all of our circumstances, and I strongly recommend developing this awareness, because it is freeing and strengthening.

11. Reading.

I hate to admit this but while I was a caregiver I did very little reading about the experiences of others. I know now that doing that would have helped me understand more fully what was happening in Carl. It also would have helped me to realize the differences in my situation from the lives of others. It would also have helped me to focus on the *now* rather than worry about what might be happening next. It would have been informative, comforting, healing, and saving. I have done a lot of reading since so I guess the truism, "better late than never" stands.

Now I strongly recommend reading during your caregiving years. These are some of the books that I have read and that I believe might be helpful to you. New books are constantly being written, so be on the lookout for them.

The Alzheimer's Caregiving Puzzle: Putting Together the Pieces,
Patricia R. Callone and Connie Kudlacek; Demos Health, (2010).

Where Two Worlds Touch: A Spiritual Journey
Through Alzheimer's Disease, Jade C. Angelica; Skinner House Books, Boston, MA (2014).

The Cloisonné Heart: A Memoir of Love,
Maggie-Margaret Honnold; Transcendent Publishing, (2017).

Chapter 16
A Memoir and a Poem

I am closing this book with a memoir of Carl by a dear friend, Barbara Vasiloff, who is the author of *Discipline with Purpose*, a program used in schools throughout the United States, and with a poem by another dear friend, Elizabeth Jeep, who is the mother of our honorary godchildren, Colonel Edward Jeep and Emily Jeep Klingaman.

A Memory of Carl

As fate would have it, even though my college degree was in education, my first job was secretary to two writers. I began working for Carl and Janaan at the United States Catholic Conference when they were working on the *Life, Love, Joy Religious Education Series* published by Silver Burdett and Ginn. It was a good job, and I felt proud to tell my friends that I was working with authors. I always wanted to be a published author and I hoped this job of "secretary" would lead to "research writer," which was another job in the same office.

The months dragged on and the research writer stayed. Carl seemed pleased with my office skills. One day a new name plaque appeared on my desk. Under my name in bold letters was the title "Secretary." This seemed way too permanent to my liking.

So, I covered the title 'Secretary" on my newly acquired nameplate and Carl noticed it immediately. "Janaan, will you look at this?" he said. When he spoke he had a way of trying to sound incredulous, but the twinkle in his eye and slight smile on his face let me know he was privately enjoying the brashness of my actions. "I don't want to be a secretary. I'm aspiring to be an author," I told him. He laughed and told me the name plate was a gift from his mother. He never asked me to remove the tape.

This incident was one among many that told me who Carl was deep, deep down. He respected with dignity the uniqueness of persons. While he was often reserved with his physical gestures, his words brought you into his circle of intimacy. A compliment from Carl meant more than one hundred hugs. His gentle, soft-spoken manner compelled me to listen to him. I learned to understand God and God's work in the world as he shared his vast theological insights not in words but in his actions.

--- **Barb Vasiloff**

POEM

I looked in all the boxes for Carl's picture
the one that was so typical
the one with him slightly behind the others
and smiling
a sly smile--you can almost hear the chuckle
the camera around his neck
dark glasses
he was always the same as I remember
only the rest of us grew, aged,
changed a style, a hair color
in most holiday pictures
but Carl was always the same,
an anchor,
a quiet attentive presence
that made the others shine
the one more apt to listen than to talk
I found while I was looking
some pictures that he had taken
revealing the love behind his lens
revealing something we had not known about ourselves
something good
something happy
something holy and real
that he saw
and loved in us
the pictures of Carl that I found
though good
and good to have
are fragmentary
each one a glimpse of what he was
but not the whole
I never found the picture I was looking for
perhaps I never took it
but my memory has it framed
where I can always find it
and remember.

—— Elizabeth McMahon Jeep

Chapter 16

Biography

Janaan Manternach was a prolific writer of religion textbooks and single title books on catechesis, theology, prayer, meditation, children's literature, and the saints. She also wrote numerous articles for journals, newspapers, and newsletters. She co-authored with her husband, Carl J. Pfeifer, the trend-setting religion series *Life, Love, Joy*. It dramatically changed how Catholic children were taught religion. In 2005 and 2011 she co-authored and contributed to three books for caregivers of persons with Alzheimer's.

She was widely known as a lecturer on catechetics and religious education throughout the United States, Europe, Canada, Guam, and Central America. She taught summer sessions at both the Catholic University of America and St. Michael's College in Winooski, VT. She also taught courses at Theological College in Washington, D.C. and St. Mary's Seminary in Baltimore, MD.

Janaan and Carl were presented the prestigious annual award from the National Conference of Catechetical Leadership recognizing their long and illustrious contribution to catechetical ministry. They were also honored by the National Association of Parish Catechetical Directors with the Emmaus Award for Excellence in Catechesis. This award was given to them because of their international reputation and contribution to the field of catholic catechesis through writing, publishing and teaching.

Janaan was an avid collector of great art, especially the works of John August Swanson of Los Angeles, CA. That collection will be given to Loras College in Dubuque, IA upon her death. In appreciation of that gesture, Loras College presented Janaan and John August Swanson with Honorary Doctorates.

Janaan Manternach's frank writing style in expressing both her love for her husband, Carl, but also for her moments of selflessness in caring for him allows us to enter her story. Her reflections will help other spouses, partners, and children as they enter the world of suffering. Some will have this experience of caring for another once, while for several others the experience of care giving may be prolonged. The lessons of accepting people as they are and being in the present world with them are good guides to be taken from this book.

Brother Ignatius Sudol

Janaan's heartfelt and down-to-earth writing describing her journey with her husband who had Alzheimer's is a wonderful book for caretakers and those who have loved ones with this disease. The question and answer forum makes it easy to access the particular part of the journey that poses a conundrum for the caretaker. Janaan's volume will help so many and contrary to the title of her book, Janaan DID do it better.

Donna Wahlert